HELLO!
A COUNTING BOOK OF KINDNESSES

Story by HOLLIS KURMAN
Illustrations by BARROUX

Otter-Barry BOOKS

What if a place got so scary
that we had to run away...?

Hold my hand and count to ten —
together we'll make it better again!

boat

helping us on our way.

2 hands

lifting us to safety.

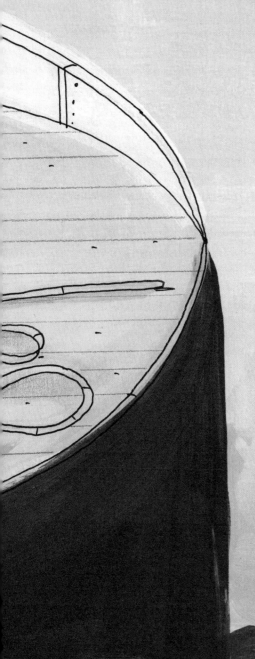

3 meals

filling us up.

4 beds
keeping us safe
and warm.

5 wishes

giving us hope.

6 books

sharing new stories
and words.

7 days
celebrating our first week
in a new land.

8 gifts
surprising us with things
we like and need.

9 signs
welcoming us to
our new school.

10 friends
making us happy!

How many ways can you think of to be kind?

WELCOME

1 one   **2** two   **3** three   **4** four   **5** five

DID YOU KNOW?

Millions of children are running away from war, floods, or other scary places. They need a safe place to live.

More than half of the world's refugees are children (over 10 million kids!).

Many child refugees have no families to take care of them.

THANKS

6 six

7 seven

8 eight

9 nine

10 ten

DO YOU WANT TO HELP
OR FIND OUT MORE?

Here are some of the many organisations helping refugees and migrants:

Amnesty International www.amnesty.org.uk

Human Rights Watch www.hrw.org

Save the Children www.savethechildren.org.uk

UNICEF www.unicef.org.uk

War Child www.warchild.org.uk

Roads to Refuge www.roads-to-refuge.com.au

RAR www.ruralaustraliansforrefugees.org.au